D0258988

Activity Book

This Book Totally Makes Stuff Grow

Maggie, Rose, Oscar and Bentley are having a totally grow
day where they will make lots of plants grow.
Did you know that most things come from a plant
that grows — even jeans and tyres and paper!

WALKER BOOKS
AND SUBSIDIARIES
LONDON · BOSTON · SYDNEY · AUCKLAND

This is Maggie, Rose, Oscar and Bentley's garden.
It has lots of stuff that grows:
flowers that smell nice,
yummy fruits and vegetables to eat,
bees that make honey, wiggly worms
and lots of other bugs and fun stuff.
Can you find any of them?

Oscar loves dirt!

Bentley loves to dig!

All activites in this book should be done with help from a grown-up.

Maggie likes the sun because it makes her feel nice and warm and her favourite colour is orange!

Rose is squirting water, which is brilliant for making plants grow – but it is fun for other stuff, too – like swimming and drinking!

What to Wear

Gardening can be messy — which means it must be fun — but you must make sure you wear things that are OK to get messy in. So, for example, you wouldn't wear new pyjamas or your dad's best suit.

STUFF TO USE

Plastic bags

Gardener's Belt

Maggie has invented a useful belt to put all her essential gardening things in.

1. Make a belt by tying two plastic bags together. Check the belt is big enough to tie around your waist. If not, tie on another plastic bag.

2. Find three more plastic bags and loop the belt through the handles.

3. Tie the belt around your waist and fill the bags with all the things you need to grow stuff.

Super Sun Visor

The sun is super important for growing stuff, including us, but too much of it can be bad for you. When it's sunny you must wear something on your head so Maggie has made super-cute sun visors for everyone to wear when gardening outside.

STUFF TO USE

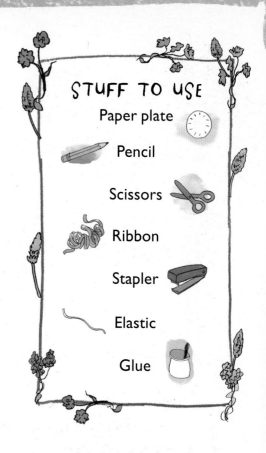

Paper plate

Pencil

Scissors

Ribbon

Stapler

Elastic

Glue

1. Hold a paper plate on your head and get a friend to mark out the shape of your head.

2. Cut the shape out, making sure the bit left at the front is wider than the bit at the back.

3. Cut a gap in the back about three fingers wide.

4. Get a grown-up to staple some elastic to each end of the gap.

5. Glue ribbon around the whole shape of the visor.

Now put it on!

STUFF TO USE

Bin liner

Cardboard box

Masking tape

Plastic bags

Gardening Tools

All good gardeners have a kit to help them make stuff grow. Maggie and Rose have made a list of all the things they think they will need and are going to make them using stuff from around the house.

Grower's Pull Box

A grower is another name for a gardener, not a person who is growing. A grower's pull box is full of the things that make stuff grow, like tools and seeds and maybe even some sandwiches — for the grower, not the plants.

1. Take a box and tear off two opposite flaps. Fold in the other two flaps.

2. Line the box with a plastic bin liner and tape down the sides.

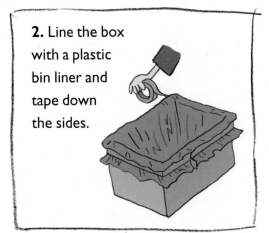

3. Get a grown-up to help you make two holes in the sides with the flaps folded down.

4. Thread some strong plastic bags through the holes and knot the ends to make handles.

Put your tools in and pull it along!

Diggers

The most fantabulous fun in the garden is digging up soil. Oscar has made his own digger to help him dig up lots of dirt!

1. Ask a grown-up to help you cut off the bottom of the bottle.

2. Mark out a semicircle shape on the bottle (as shown) and ask your grown-up to cut it out for you.

3. Have your grown-up stick bits of parcel tape over the cut edges of the bottle, in case there are any sharp bits.

4. Decorate with lots of stickers. Make other diggers by using different shaped bottles!

STUFF TO USE

Clean plastic milk bottle (no label)

Marker pen

Scissors

Parcel tape

Stickers

Watering Bottle

Water is super important for making stuff grow. Rose loves water and has found a way to make her own plant waterer.

STUFF TO USE

Clean plastic milk bottle (no label)

Scissors

Magazine

Sticky tape

1. Ask a grown-up to help you pierce the top of the bottle with about twenty small holes.

2. Cut out the letters of your name from a magazine and stick them to the milk bottle, below the handle.

3. Cover your name with sticky tape to make it waterproof.

STUFF TO USE

Big bucket /
container

Paper

Pencil

Stickers

Box /container

Making Compost

Soil is super important for growing stuff but compost can make it even better. Compost is made from things you would think are horrible like old vegetable peelings and eggshells but soil loves these things. It is easy to make compost but you will need a grown-up to help. You put the vegetable peelings and eggshells into the compost – not the grown-ups!!

1. First you'll need a big container to store your compost in. You could ask a grown-up to get a special composter, or you can use an old dustbin with holes in the bottom (get a grown-up to make the holes for you). Find a suitable place to put it outside the house.

2. Make a list of the right things to put into your compost. Rose has made a list of good stuff.

Good stuff
Paper, dry leaves and twigs, tea bags, coffee dregs, eggshells, vegetable peelings, bits of cardboard.

Oscar has made a list of bad things that you shouldn't put in your compost.

Bad stuff
Meat, fish, bread, plastic, cooked food, magazine pages, fresh weeds.

3. Find another container to sit next to your kitchen bin and decorate it brightly with stickers. Use this to collect GOOD STUFF for your compost bin (put your list next to it to remind you what can go in).

GOOD STUFF!

The Future
Jan Feb Mar Apr
May Jun Jul Aug
Sept Oct Nov Dec

4. Add your good stuff each day to your compost bin. Ask a grown-up to help you mix it up every couple of weeks. It takes quite a long time to turn into compost – about three months. Once it's ready, put it on the garden and watch new stuff grow!

Muddy Experiments

Soil takes thousands of years to make and is absolutely full of living things. Not big things but tiny little creatures that can only be seen with a microscope. In one spoonful of soil there could be nearly 7,000 of these tiny things. Join the gang with their experiment to see how many living things they can find.

STUFF TO USE

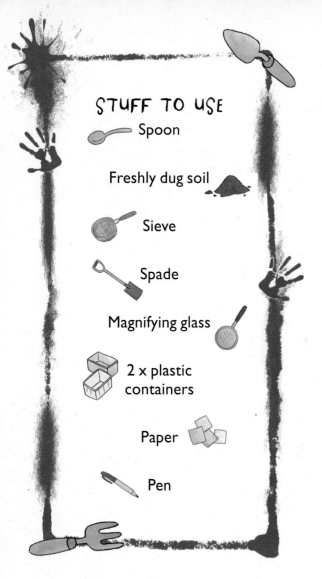

Spoon

Freshly dug soil

Sieve

Spade

Magnifying glass

2 x plastic containers

Paper

Pen

1. Using a spade, dig up some soil. The deeper you go, the more likely it is that you'll find creatures in it.

2. Place a spade full of soil in one of your containers.

3. Take a spoonful of dirt and shake it through the sieve over your other container.

4. Look at your soil through the magnifying glass. See how many creatures you can find.

5. Is there a creature left in the sieve? If there is, write down its name, or draw a picture of it to keep a record. If you don't know what it is, try to find out.

6. Don't forget to put the creatures back in the soil when you've finished.

What creatures can you find?

Potty Potatoes

Bentley loves to dig and his favourite thing to dig for is potatoes. Maggie is planting some potatoes so Bentley will have something to dig for in the summer. These potatoes won't be in a big field, they'll be in a pot so Maggie calls them Potty Potatoes.

STUFF TO USE

- A few old potatoes that have started to sprout shoots
- Soil
- Water
- Big plastic bucket / container
- Stones or gravel

1. Put your old potatoes in the sun for about two weeks to harden.

2. Take your bucket or container and ask a grown-up to make some drainage holes in the bottom of it for you.

3. Fill the bottom with a layer of stones and gravel – this is to help with drainage.

4. Add a small layer of soil – about 20 centimetres deep.

5. Place three of your potatoes in the bucket. Make sure they have enough room between them to grow and that the sprouts are facing up.

6. Now add some more soil, just enough to cover the potatoes fully.

7. Find a good spot for your potatoes that is warm but not too sunny. Keep checking them to see if any shoots appear. When they do, cover them with more soil. Do this until your container is full.

8. Make sure you water your plants and keep them well covered from the sun. Potatoes can go green in the sun and then they are poisonous!

9. When your plants start to flower it means your potatoes are ready – yay!

Now gently dig them up and wash all the dirt off them.

Potato Faces

When you have grown your potatoes
the best thing to do is eat them!
Rose loves to make crazy faces with potatoes.

STUFF TO USE

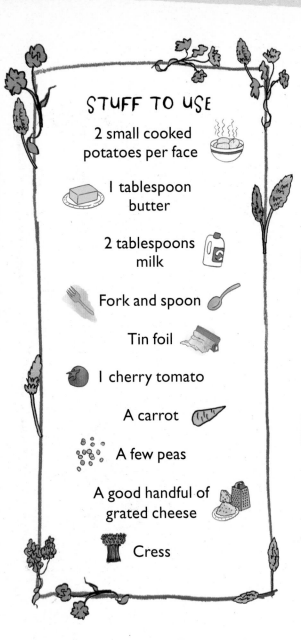

2 small cooked potatoes per face

1 tablespoon butter

2 tablespoons milk

Fork and spoon

Tin foil

1 cherry tomato

A carrot

A few peas

A good handful of grated cheese

Cress

1. Put your cooked potatoes in a bowl with butter and milk and mash with a fork until smooth.

2. Spoon the mashed potatoes onto a piece of tin foil and make a face shape.

3. Ask a grown-up to cut a cherry tomato in half to use as eyes.

4. Put a pea in the centre of each half tomato to make a pupil.

5. Ask a grown-up to cut a piece of carrot for the nose.

6. Use the remaining peas to make a big smiley mouth.

7. Carefully sprinkle the grated cheese all over the face.

8. Ask a grown-up to grill your potato face for 10–15 minutes.

9. Ask a grown-up to take him out of the oven and pop him on a plate. Now add your cressy hair and eat!

Mmmmmmmm, delicious!

Wiggly Wormery

Worms love soil and soil loves worms because worms help soil to become better to grow things in. You can dig in the soil to find worms — they are long and slimy and don't have any eyes! Oscar once ate a worm to see what it tasted like — eewww! (He said it wasn't as good as chicken.)

STUFF TO USE

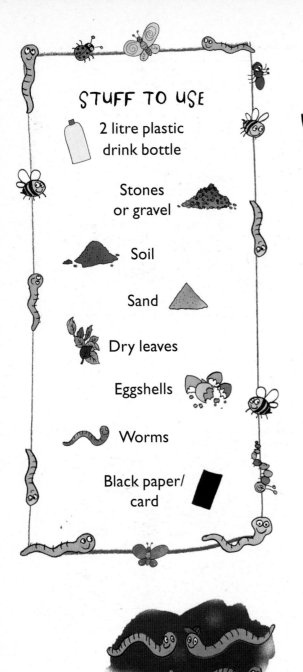

- 2 litre plastic drink bottle
- Stones or gravel
- Soil
- Sand
- Dry leaves
- Eggshells
- Worms
- Black paper/card

1. Ask a grown-up to carefully cut the top off your plastic bottle.

2. Place a small layer of stones in the bottom.

stones

3. Layer in some soil to give a good base, pat it down and make sure it's nice and damp.

soil

4. Next add a thin layer of sand and then another layer of soil.

sand

5. Now add your dry leaves and eggshells.

6. Add your worms – they will burrow straight away to escape the light

7. Wrap the bottle in the black paper so the worms don't get too much light.

Bye, bye wiggly worms!

Make sure you keep your wormery damp – but don't put too much water in or your worms will drown. Keep worms for a maximum of two weeks and then return them to your garden along with the newly fertilized soil they have made.

Water Makes Things Grow!

All plants need to be watered to make them grow, but there are some that ONLY need water to make them grow.

Crazy Carrot Top Forest

A carrot top forest is easy to grow and Maggie can show you how to do it.

STUFF TO USE

10 carrots that have started to sprout shoots

Shallow plastic container (non-leaky)

Water

1. Ask a grown-up to cut roughly 2 centimetres off the top of each carrot.

2. Arrange the carrot tops in your container and add a small amount of water.

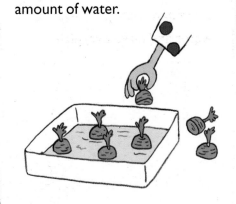

3. Place them on a sunny windowsill and watch them grow!

Your carrot top forest will look lovely and bushy, but it won't grow carrots again. To do this, you'll need carrot seeds.

Alfalfa
A type of sprout that's actually yummy!

STUFF TO USE

 Alfalfa seeds

Shallow plastic container (non-leaky)

Water

Kitchen roll

1. Place some kitchen roll in the bottom of your container and moisten it with water.

2. Sprinkle seeds all over the kitchen roll.

3. Leave the container in a warm, sunny place and watch the seeds grow. Remember to keep them watered.

Mung Beans

Tasty and also easy-peasy to grow!

1. Wash your beans and put them in the jam jar. Fill it with water and leave overnight.

STUFF TO USE

 Mung beans

Jam jar

 Water

Clean tights

 Rubber band

Kitchen roll

2. Cover the top of the jam jar with a piece cut from the tights. Secure it with a rubber band.

3. Drain and rinse the beans twice a day.

4. After five days, the beans are ready to eat. Rinse them and lay them out on kitchen roll to dry off. Eat immediately.

Rainbow Sprout Bagels

The gang love food and they have invented this scrummy bagel sandwich using the things Maggie grew with water.

STUFF TO USE

 Bagel

 1 small carrot, grated

 2 tablespoons cream cheese per bagel

A handful of mung bean sprouts

A handful of alfalfa

4–5 cherry tomatoes

 Bowl and spoon

1. Get a grown-up to slice your bagel in half.

2. Scoop out the soft bready middle of the bagel with your hands.

3. Put the cream cheese and carrot into a bowl.

4. Squash the tomatoes into the bowl – make sure you squeeze all the insides out.

5. Add the mung bean sprouts and the alfalfa and mix into a paste.

6. Spoon the mixture back into the hollowed out bagel.

Delicious!

Going on a Bug Hunt

Plants aren't the only important things in the garden — bugs are super important, too! They can also help stuff grow and the gang are going on a bug hunt to see how many they can see. They won't touch them, though, as some are not as nice as they look.

STUFF TO USE

Two toilet rolls

Sticky tape

String

Bug Binoculars

Bugs are hard to find — but these super binos will make it much easier!

1. Wrap some sticky tape around the two toilet rolls to hold them together.

2. At one end, ask a grown-up to make a hole on either side.

3. Measure out enough string to be able to hang the binoculars loosely around your neck. Thread the string through the holes in your binoculars and tie the ends in knots to secure it.

Bug-Hunter's Notebook

To record what you find, you need a bug book.

1. Cut your tracing paper into four even pieces.

2. Stack your pieces in a pile and punch a hole in the top corner. Fasten the pieces together with string.

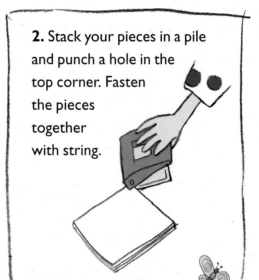

STUFF TO USE

A4 tracing paper

Hole punch

String

Pencil

Magnifying glass

3. Trace the bugs from the picture below, then go and see how many you can find.

You can see most bugs without a magnifying glass, but Maggie likes to use one to look more closely.

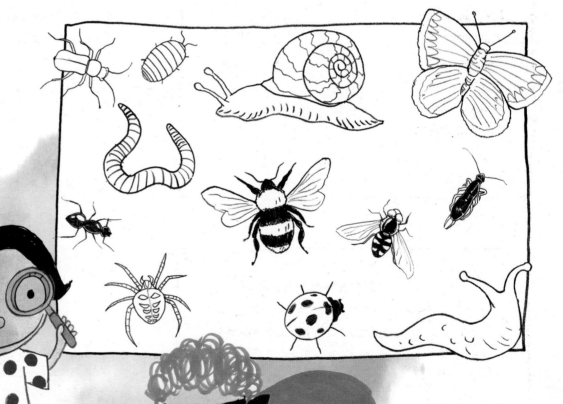

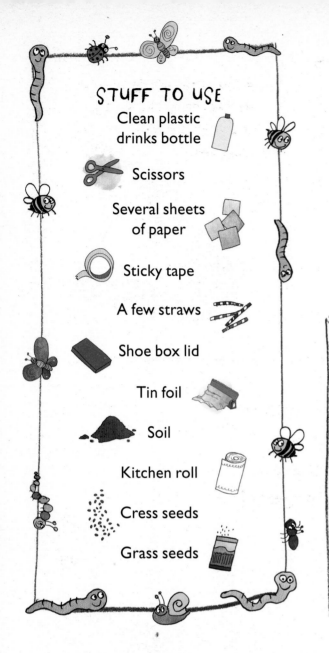

STUFF TO USE

- Clean plastic drinks bottle
- Scissors
- Several sheets of paper
- Sticky tape
- A few straws
- Shoe box lid
- Tin foil
- Soil
- Kitchen roll
- Cress seeds
- Grass seeds

Bug Hotel

Bugs like dark, safe places where they can hide from bigger creatures in the garden that want to eat them. Rose is making a bug hotel to see if she can attract some bugs into her garden — but she won't make the bugs pay to stay there!

I. Ask an adult to cut both ends off the plastic bottle.

2. If the width of your paper is greater than the length of your plastic bottle, trim each piece of paper to just under the length of the bottle.

3. Roll up each piece of paper into a small tube and stick it with tape.

4. Tuck the paper tubes into the bottle.

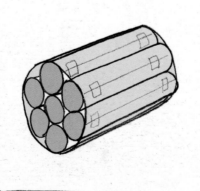

5. Cut the straws to size and poke them into the spaces in the bottle.

6. Cover the shoe box lid in tin foil to make it waterproof, then fill it with soil.

7. Nestle the bug hotel into the soil.

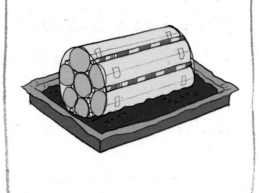

8. Cover the hotel with a few layers of damp kitchen roll and sprinkle it with cress seeds.

9. Sprinkle the soil with grass seeds and decorate the rest of the tray with twigs and leaves from your garden.

Place the hotel in the garden and watch it grow — keep it watered and see how many bugs it attracts!

Fruity Pips

Yummy fruits have seeds which we also call pips. It's the pips that make the fruit grow in the first place, so Maggie, Rose, Oscar and Bentley are trying to grow some fruit of their own from pips they find in their fruit.

STUFF TO USE

Lots of different types of fruit (e.g. apples, oranges, melon and clementines)

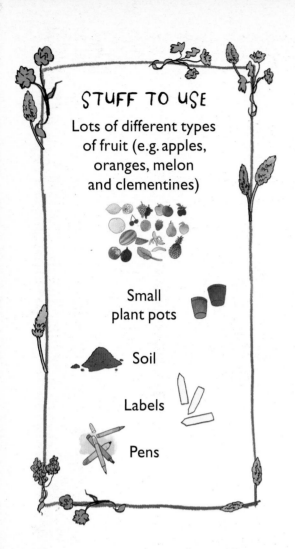

Small plant pots

Soil

Labels

Pens

1. Look at all your different types of fruit and see if you can find any seeds. You will need a grown-up to help you cut things up. Once you have found your seeds, do an experiment to see which ones will grow.

2. Gather a few different plant pots and plant a different type of seed in each one.

3. Label them and leave them in a warm, sunny place to see which ones grow. Remember to water them.

Don't forget the rules for growing things

1. Put your seeds in a pot of soil.

2. Check regularly to see if it needs water – but don't water it too much!

3. Keep your plants nice and warm in the sun.

Don't waste any of the fruit you used to find the pips – make Oscar's crazy fruit squash.

1. Chop or break up all the remaining fruit in a bowl.

2. Using a fork, squash as much of the fruit as you can!

3. Pour over some yogurt and drizzle with honey. EAT!

Sizzling Sunflowers

Sunflowers love the sun – and they even look a bit like it! They are also very tall because they're always stretching up to reach it. The gang are having a competition to see who can grow the tallest sunflower.

STUFF TO USE

Plant pot with holes in the bottom for drainage

Soil

Sunflower seeds

Water

Wooden cane

Bits of string

1. Fill your pot with soil.

2. Push your finger into the soil and make a little hole.

3. Choose a seed and place it in the hole. Cover it with soil and water lightly.

4. Place your pot in a sunny spot and water it regularly. In about a week you will see some shoots.

5. As your sunflower grows, you will need to put a cane in and tie your sunflower stem to it for support. You may even need to transfer it to a bigger pot. Ask a grown-up to help you. You will have to wait fourteen weeks for it to flower!

Whose flower wins the competition?

Giant Worm Racing

Real worms are really slow. They have a lot of important work to do in the soil, so racing them can take for ever. Maggie, Rose, Oscar and Bentley have made up a super fun pretend worm race.

STUFF TO USE

Old stockings

Newspaper

Masking tape

Balls of string

Lollipop sticks

Make Your Worm

1. Stuff your stocking with scrunched up newspaper until you have a nice big worm.

2. Tie the end tightly with string, but don't cut the string – leave it in a ball.

Make Your Track

1. Decide where the start and finish lines are going to be. Mark them with two different lines of string and tape the ends down.

2. Lay the worms down at the start line and unwind the ball of string to the finish line. Now cut the string and tie it to your lollipop stick.

How to Play the Game

Race time!
After a count of three,
wind the worms in as fast as you can,
wrapping the string around the stick.

Who will win?!

Did You Know?

Lots of everyday things come from plants: jeans and T-shirts, chocolate, rubber, paper, popcorn, bread. Can you find out which plant each of these comes from?

The longest earthworm is the African giant earthworm, which can grow up to 6.7 metres long. Which is as long as four grown-ups standing on top of each other!

What other amazing facts can you find out? Use your computer to look some up.

The tallest sunflower in the world was grown in Holland — it measured almost 8 metres tall. That's the same as nearly seven Oscars!

Ladybirds are the most commonly used form of pest control. One adult ladybird can eat as many as fifty aphids a day!